The BUMPER BOOK of BOB

For Alison Eldred,
my trusty co-pilot — S.B.

A TEMPLAR BOOK

First published in the UK in 2011 by Templar Publishing,
an imprint of The Templar company Limited,
The Granary, North Street, Dorking, Surrey, RH4 1DN, UK
www.templarco.co.uk

copyright © 2002, 2008,
2009, 2010 and 2011 by Simon Bartram

1 3 5 7 9 10 8 6 4 2
0811 007

ISBN 978-1-84877-054-6

Designed by Mike Jolley and Manhar Chauhan
Edited by Libby Hamilton and Jenny Broom

Printed in Malaysia

SIMON
BARTRAM

The BUMPER BOOK
of
BOB

templar publishing

Welcome to my bumper book!

Dear Readers,

Ever since Simon started writing stories about me and my job as Man on the Moon, he's been getting lots of letters from interested readers. Barry (my furry best friend) and I were surprised that they find our humdrum daily life so interesting, but Simon suggested that we make a bumper book to answer lots of their questions.

As you never know when you'll be stuck on a long space-trip, we've added some puzzles and colouring in, and a story by Simon about our newest exciting adventure. We've even added a few of our favourite recipes for everyone to try!

So we hope our readers enjoy this bumper book (and Queen Battleaxe doesn't see it, as we haven't been very nice about her).

Love,

Barry, *Bob* and Simon!

contents

Stories, Poems and Stuff

Fascinating Facts

Astro-Activities

This is Bob

Bob has given us a sneaky peek at his working day and let us in on a few of his most useful spaceman hints and tips.

I always carry my passport and my cosmic map book. You never know when the navigation thingmajig might pack up!

SPACE A-Z

These are my casual clothes. It's very important to look tip-top tickety-boo at all times.

This is my trusty Man on the Moon suit, mainly made of super-rubber.

My Tools of the Trade

1. Alien-translating machine. Purely for show – I'll never need to use it since there are no such things as aliens.

2. Note book. Great for sketching odd-looking Moon tourists.

3. Mobile phone. Very handy indeed, although texting with space gloves on can prove most tricky.

4. Flask of tea. Never, but NEVER zoom anywhere without it.

My Favourite Things in All The Universe

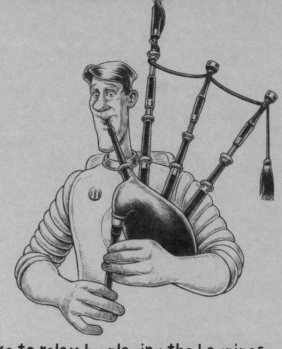

I love Barry, my Best-Ever Friend. The moment we met was magical, even though he did scuff my suit a little.

I like to relax by playing the bagpipes. Barry isn't so keen but what do dogs know about music? I'm also fond of the banjo and the pump organ.

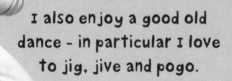

I also enjoy a good old dance - in particular I love to jig, jive and pogo.

I have a penchant for tank tops and moon pants. Neither need to be expensive if you shop around or use a catalogue.

At the end of a long day, a bath with my rocket-shaped soap and moon-shaped sponge is just the ticket.

Space Picnic

Use the stickers in the middle of the book to decorate
this picture of Bob's busy day on the Moon.

Lunar Lament

I'M A SUBJECT NEVER PAINTED,
I'M A PLACE WHERE NO ONE GOES.
I'VE NO GLOWING REPUTATION,
I'VE A FACE THAT NO ONE KNOWS.

I'M NOT GAZED UPON BY SWEETHEARTS,
HOWLING WOLVES CARE NOT FOR ME.
I'M SWITCHED OFF, BLOWN OUT,
EXTINGUISHED,
I DON'T SPARKLE ON THE SEA.

BUT THINGS COULD CHANGE
FOR ME ONE DAY —
I COULD BE FAMOUS SOON.
TILL THEN I'LL QUIETLY REMAIN,
THE DARK SIDE OF THE MOON.

Bob's Ballads

Cryptic Crossword

IT'S A TERRIBLY PESKY CROSSWORD,
ITS COMPLETION IS WELL OVERDUE.
MY BRAIN IS FRIED,
FOR MONTHS I'VE TRIED
TO SOLVE THE VERY LAST CLUE.

IT'S A FOUR-LETTER
SPACE-THEMED PUZZLER.
I'M DESPERATE TO SUSS IT OUT SOON.
IT BEGINS WITH 'M'
AND IT ENDS WITH 'N'
AND PERFECTLY RHYMES WITH 'SPOON'.

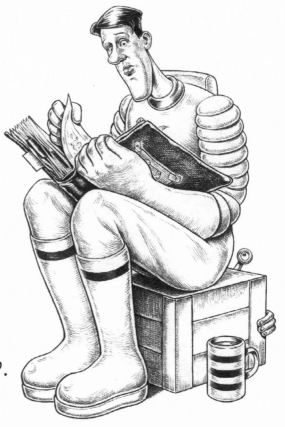

Say Cheese!

COLOUR IN THIS SCENE FROM QUEEN BATTLEAXE'S MOON-PARTY. (THIS ONE'S TRICKY!)

Bob's Spectacular Galaxo-Facts

1. The Sun

Hotter than wearing three tank tops and brighter than looking at a lamp through a pair of binoculars, the Sun really does light up our Solar System.

The Moon is about here!

4.

5.

6.

3.

1.

2.

2. Mercury

Next to the Sun, Mercury can get very hot. It's best not to go there at all but if you must, take Bob's advice: stuff your pants with ice cubes and don't bother to wear a vest.

3. Venus

Officially the planet of 'lurve', Venus is the tip-top no. 1 destination for soppy girls. Bob prefers to steer clear of it altogether.

4. Earth

Bob is from Earth and so are you, unless you're an alien, which you're not, so you are!

5. Mars

Bob often visits his friend Billy here, meeting him at the Mars (Milkshake) Bar, where they sell every flavour of milkshake imaginable. Each trip, Bob orders their delicious I-can't-believe-it's-not-tea flavoured shake.

6. Jupiter

This massive planet has lots and lots of moons. Vacuuming them all takes until after three in the afternoon. This would not suit Bob at all as there'd be no time left for practising the bagpipes.

The Moon

It takes Bob fifteen minutes to get from Lunar Hill launch-pad to the Moon. Then again, he knows all of the shortcuts, so it might take you a bit longer.

7. Saturn

Saturn's nine rings are mainly made up of rocks and ice, but also include discarded cosmic junk. On a recent visit, Bob was delighted to salvage an old pair of wellies and an armchair for his shed.

8. Uranus

This gassy planet is a really pongy place to visit. Bob advises tourists of a fragile nature to have handy at least one super-strength nose peg and perhaps some smelling salts.

9. Neptune

Although extremely cold, Neptune remains popular with tourists because of its famous miniature train. When Bob rides it he always wears a tank top over his spacesuit and a woolly hat on top of his helmet.

10. Pluto

Bob rarely visits this dwarf planet (not a proper planet, but Bob doesn't hold that against it). It's dark and cold and so far away that it's almost impossible to make it home in time to watch Goal of the Day.

Bob's Interesting and Surprising Moon-Facts

One of the biggest myths about the Moon is the idea that aliens can be found there. Bob has been working on the Moon for years and he can definitely confirm that there are absolutely no aliens there. Not a single one.

Walking around the Moon on stilts is one of Bob's special skills. Last year he smashed his own record, completing the route in under seven hours and forty-three minutes.

There are 14,678 craters on the Moon, each one charming in its own way. After careful consideration, Bob gave crater 8,764 the prestigious Crater of the Year Award, for its roominess and delicately cheesy odour.

BOB'S SCARY BOSS, TARANTULA VAN TRUMPET, LOVES TO DOODLE ALL KINDS OF STRANGE THINGS DURING IMPORTANT MEETINGS...

Doodle Time

WHAT EXTRA-TERRESTRIAL DOODLES CAN YOU DO?

A	C	E	W	F	C	C	E	B	U
X	O	D	X	V	H	U	W	N	N
G	R	H	A	B	E	C	T	D	D
Y	N	B	A	R	R	Y	D	F	E
A	E	D	L	O	R	M	H	E	R
F	D	Q	W	U	Y	I	A	G	P
R	B	V	I	P	B	E	S	D	A
D	E	G	G	Y	U	I	P	A	N
I	E	E	S	J	N	K	A	B	T
O	F	H	L	K	T	L	C	N	S
R	S	A	M	C	L	B	E	O	Z
E	L	C	N	M	Y	O	S	T	I
T	I	S	P	O	P	C	H	T	J
S	C	R	A	T	E	R	I	U	Z
A	E	R	K	A	N	L	P	B	Q

oh, My Word!

can you find these words in the panel? They might be spelt backwards and could be read upwards, downwards or diagonally, just to keep you on your toes!

ASTEROID

CRATER

BARRY

SPACE SHIP

BICYCLE

BUTTON BADGE

CHERRY BUN

UNDERPANTS

CORNED BEEF SLICE

(ANSWERS ON PAGE 60.)

This is Barry

It's a one-of-a-kind job, being the best-ever friend to the Man on the Moon. Here's a closer look at Barry, Bob's number one companion.

IDENTITY CARD

NAME: Barry

OCCUPATION: Best-Ever Friend

LICENCE TO DRIVE: No need for a spaceship with six speedy legs

PLANET OF RESIDENCE: Earth

ALIEN ACTIVITY? No comment

CURRENT LOCATION: Bone burying in crater 204 on the Moon

W.A.P.A.

WORLDWIDE ASTRONAUTS' PETS' ASSOCIATION

often his breath stinks to high heaven. More than once Bob has fainted at the boney stench.

Bob can't remember a time when Barry's tail wasn't wagging nineteen to the dozen.

Six legs make Barry excellent at jumping, bouncing and flea-scratching.

Barry might have only one eye, but that's never bothered Bob. In fact, Barry is not sure that Bob's even noticed.

Inside here is Barry's heart of gold, which belongs to his one true friend, Bob. (And maybe to his rubber duck a little bit, too.)

22

And Bob's Other Super-Chums

IDENTITY CARD

NAME: Billy

OCCUPATION: Man on Mars

LICENCE TO DRIVE: Mars Car

PLANET OF RESIDENCE: Mars

ALIEN ACTIVITY? once took part in a penalty shoot-out with a little green goalkeeper

CURRENT LOCATION: The Mars (Milkshake) Bar

W.A.A.
WORLDWIDE ASTRONAUTS' ASSOCIATION

IDENTITY CARD

NAME: Cousin Dougal

OCCUPATION: Deep-Sea Diver

LICENCE TO DRIVE: Submarine

PLANET OF RESIDENCE: Earth

MARINE ACTIVITY? on the same darts team as Neptune, three mermen and a pirate ghost

CURRENT LOCATION: Atlantis

UND.I.E.S.
UNDERWATER INTREPID EXPLORERS' SOCIETY

IDENTITY CARD

NAME: Mr Nigel Carruthers

OCCUPATION: Galaxobot 3000, "Happy to Help"

LICENCE TO DRIVE: Moon Buggy

PLANET OF RESIDENCE: Earth

ALIEN ACTIVITY? delighted to serve humans, aliens, monsters and giants

CURRENT LOCATION: the Scottish Highlands, writing poetry which he sends to Bob.

D.R.O.ID.
DOMESTIC ROBOTS' ORGANISATION IDENTIFICATION

IDENTITY CARD

NAME: Sam

OCCUPATION: Man on Saturn

LICENCE TO DRIVE: SUV (Saturn Utility Vehicle)

PLANET OF RESIDENCE: Saturn

ALIEN ACTIVITY? doesn't like to discuss it

CURRENT LOCATION: with his friends at the Mars (Milkshake) Bar

W.A.A.
WORLDWIDE ASTRONAUTS' ASSOCIATION

Space Tourist's Map

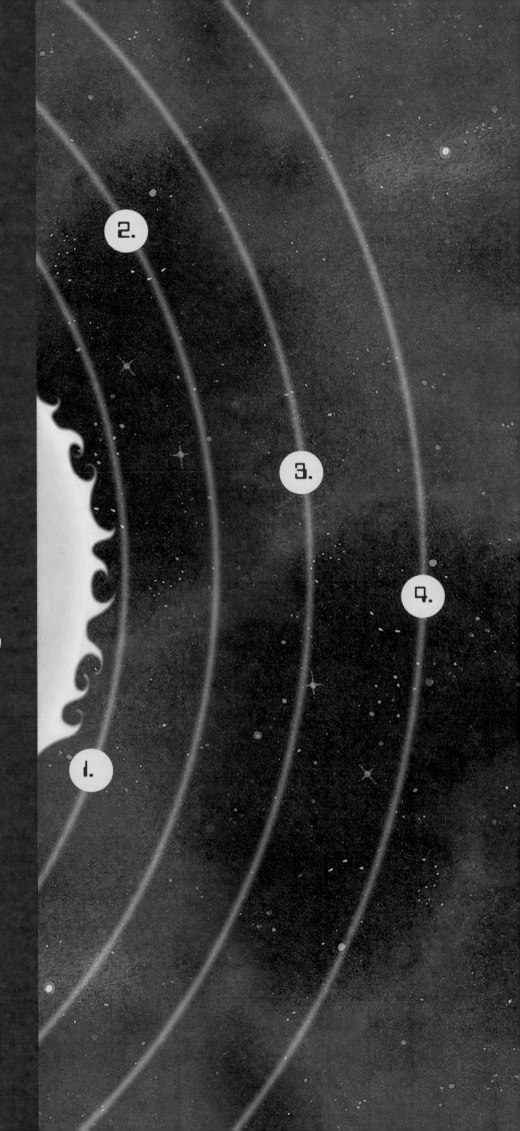

Use the stickers in the middle of this book to complete this picture of our Solar System. If you want to check the order of the planets, turn to my super space guide on pages 18 and 19.

Remember, to make this a proper guide for space tourists, you'll need to include the football stadium on Neptune and the button badge factory on Uranus. Both are fun days out for the whole family (though not as good as a trip to the Moon, obviously).

2.

3.

4.

1.

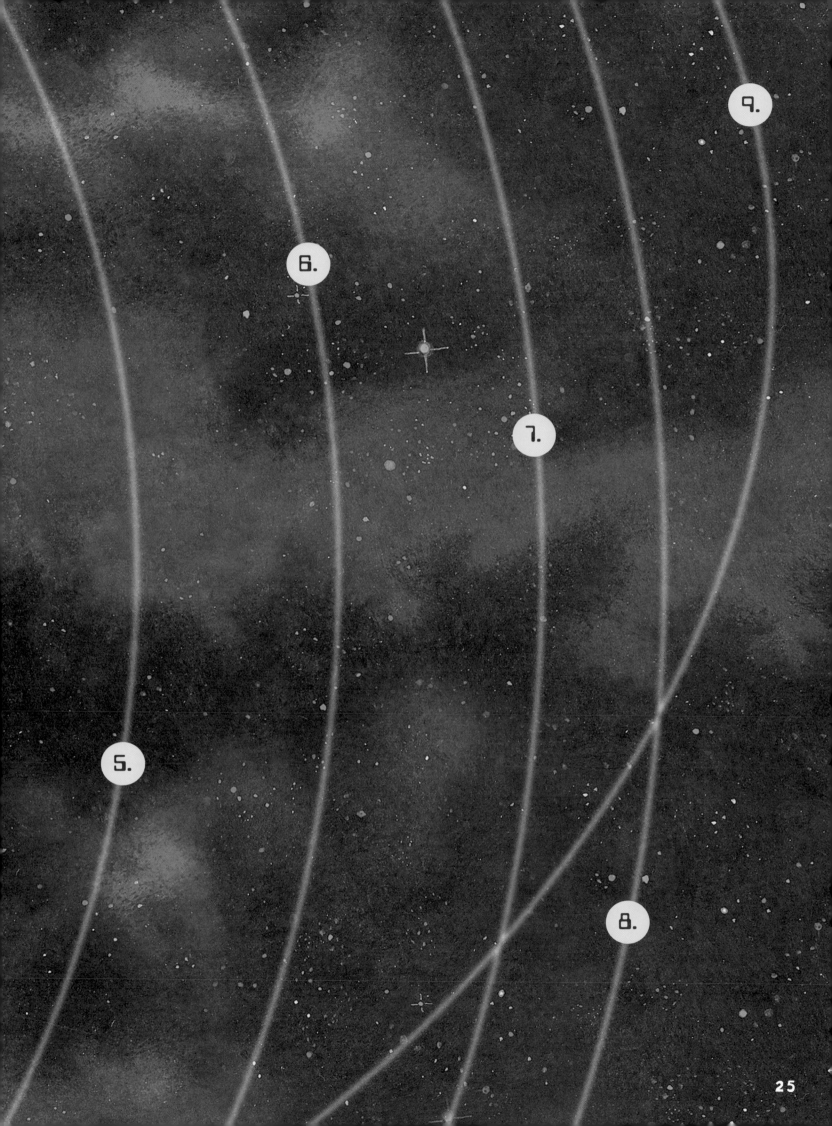

BOB SAVES THE WORLD

STARRING BOB, BARRY AND THEIR REMOTE CONTROL FLYING SAUCER

Barry and Bob were delighted. It had been three long months since Bob had ordered it from the factory on Venus and now, finally, their brand spanking new state-of-the-art remote control flying saucer had been delivered to the Moon. It was a lot smaller than it had seemed in the catalogue, but even so, they were cock-a-hoop.

Bob just couldn't wait to try it out and without even checking his instruction manual he plunged down the red-coloured 'START' button on the complicated remote control. The flying saucer didn't move an inch.

"Hmmm," he said to Barry. "There must be some kind of malfunction type problem with the remote control thingummyjig. Not to worry. Easily fixed!"

Certainly he seemed to be right. After a brief fiddle and twiddle with his screwdriver Bob once again pressed the red button. This time, dramatically, the flying saucer shot upwards and began to soar and swoop in perfect time

with Bob's busy fingers. It was wonderful. Under Bob's command it danced among the stars. It raced with comets. It looped around Saturn's rings. And for Barry it was so much better than chasing a boring old stick.

When home time came they weren't ready for the fun to end. Bob thought perhaps they could take it with them. They could fly it in the garden or in the park or even on the beach. Unfortunately, however, it was just too bulky to squeeze into the rocket.

"Well," said Bob, "we'll simply have to navigate it home from here using the remote control whatchamacallit. Should be a doddle!"

And so, having scrawled in marker pen 'PROPERTY OF BOB' on its rear end, Bob called upon all of his spacey expertise to skilfully direct his flying saucer homewards. Then, having packed up his lunar bits and bobs, he and Barry blasted off home themselves.

Just before they reached Earth, as Bob was preparing to land, a panicky voice blared out over the space radio: "INVASION, INVASION! THE ALIENS ARE COMING. REPEAT: THE ALIENS ARE COMING! THE END IS NIGH!"

Bob couldn't understand it – was this some kind of joke? As he cycled home from Lunar Hill launch-pad with Barry in his basket, there was an eerie quiet across the countryside and in town he noticed the streets were deserted. Abandoned cars and buses clogged up the road. Shutters were down. Curtains were drawn. The deathly strange silence was broken

crater caper

Use the stickers to show what Bob might find in crater 367.

The Space Race!

CAN YOU HELP BOB FLY HIS ROCKET HOME TO EARTH?

Moonlight Sonata

COLOUR IN THIS SCENE OF BOB RELAXING WITH HIS BAGPIPES.

Spacecraft Spotter's Guide

Look carefully and you just might spot all sorts of weird and wonderful spacecraft in the night sky. Here are some of Bob's favourites.

Steinbeck Trimble's Mobile Library Rocket

Amazingly, this rocket contains every book ever written anywhere in the universe. Most astronauts favour pop star annuals or novels about clever detectives.

Queen Battleaxe's Regal Rocket

This is probably the poshest rocket ever designed. It has a banqueting suite, two disco toilets and room for a small pony. Rumour has it that this rocket runs on liquid gold.

Donut Apollo Shuttle Pod

At 75p per return trip, this is still the cheapest mode of lunar transport. Watch out for the onboard tuck shop though - choc ices are particuarly pricey.

Galaxobot Moon Buggy

A reliable little runner, this can make an economical family spacecraft. With a bit of wheeling and dealing, a Galaxobot chauffur could be included in the price.

Bob's Rocket

Of course, none of the other spacecraft profiled here come anywhere close to rivalling Bob's for style and sheer panache.

Nose Cone
Protects the rocket from the heat on re-entry to the Earth's atmosphere.

Cockpit
Where Bob flies the rocket. It is mostly full of moon souvenirs and collected rubbish.

Lumpy Yellow Band
This has no use. It is there just to make the rocket look cool!

Rocket Boosters
These shoot flames which propel the rocket forward.

37

Poet's corner

Another corker from Bob's Book of Ballads.

MIDNIGHT SNACK

THOUGH THE SAMPLE THEY GOT
WAS A SIZEABLE CHUNK,
DURING THE RIGOROUS TESTING
IT SHRUNK AND IT SHRUNK.

THEY GRATED AND SLICED IT
AND CUBED IT UP TOO.
THEY MELTED IT DOWN
INTO GOOEY FONDUE.

THEY TEAMED IT WITH PICKLES,
TOMATOES AND CHIVES —
THEY TRIED IT WITH HAM
AND ESCAPED WITH THEIR LIVES.

IT ALL WENT TO PLAN
WHEN THEY STIRRED IT THROUGH PASTA,
AND GRILLED ON FRESH PIZZAS
IT PROVED NO DISASTER.

IN TRIANGULAR SEGMENTS
OR SLICES OR BLOCKS,
IT COULD SMELL RATHER PLEASANT
OR STINK LIKE OLD SOCKS.

BE IT SPRINGY OR CRUMBLY
OR PEPPERED WITH HOLES,
IT WAS TIP-TOP WITH CRACKERS,
BAGUETTES OR BREAD ROLLS.

WHEN THE TESTS WERE COMPLETED
THE BOFFINS WERE PLEASED
TO CONFIRM THAT THE MOON
WAS INDEED MADE OF CHEESE!

SO NOW IF YOU'RE PECKISH
IN THE DEAD OF THE NIGHT
JUST CLIMB IN YOUR ROCKET
AND TAKE A SHORT FLIGHT.

ENSURE YOU'RE PREPARED
WITH A KNIFE OR A GRATER
(ESSENTIAL TO SLICE OFF
THE RIM OF A CRATER).

THEN RETURN TO YOUR KITCHEN
FOR THE SNACK YOU LOVE MOST —
A SLICE OF DELICIOUS
GRILLED MOON-CHEESE ON TOAST!

Know Your Aliens!

Here are some funny pictures and descriptions sent in by fans with vivid imaginations. Of course, Barry and I can confirm aliens don't really exist.

The Mushy-Mushy Sop-Sop

This alien falls in love at the drop of a hat. It can be difficult to tell a male from a female though - just look at Keith here and you can probably see what we mean.

Always sure to be sporting a stylish tank top

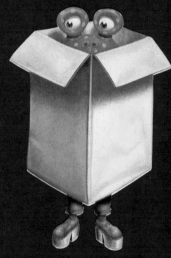

The Super [Little Green] Man

Where there's trouble, he'll b there... although it might tal him a while as he can't fly.

Lanky-Planks

These are the tallest known aliens. Finding a pair of extra, extra, extra long trousers is a lifelong problem for them all.

The Lesser Spotted Box-Dweller

This species has spots that are only visible when they feel nervous (which is nearly all of the time).

Mysterious Tub-Dwellers

Not much is known about these aliens, apart from the fact that they are squeaky-clean.

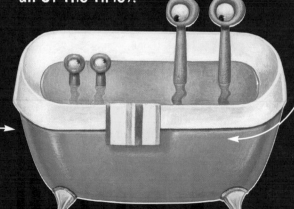

They often share baths due to the lack of water in space.

Toobeetoos

These aliens are almost impossible to tell apart, as you can see with these two individuals, Clive and Clive. Inside their fashionable platform shoes they can store small cakes.

People say aliens pop up all over the place. What a joke!

The Mod Bod

There is no alien in the universe who loves button badges more than the Mod Bod.

The Tie Pie

These fellows are named after their two great loves: eye-catching neckwear and savoury baked goods!

Alien Food

Aliens are huge fans of cherry buns and pizzas, but they are truly terrified of sprouts and prunes. Wait a minute...

...there were definitely two cherry buns here earlier!

Ooballyballies

Often seen playing at the Stardust Arena on Neptune, an Ooballyballie in top shape can bounce up to 2,134 times per minute.

crossword

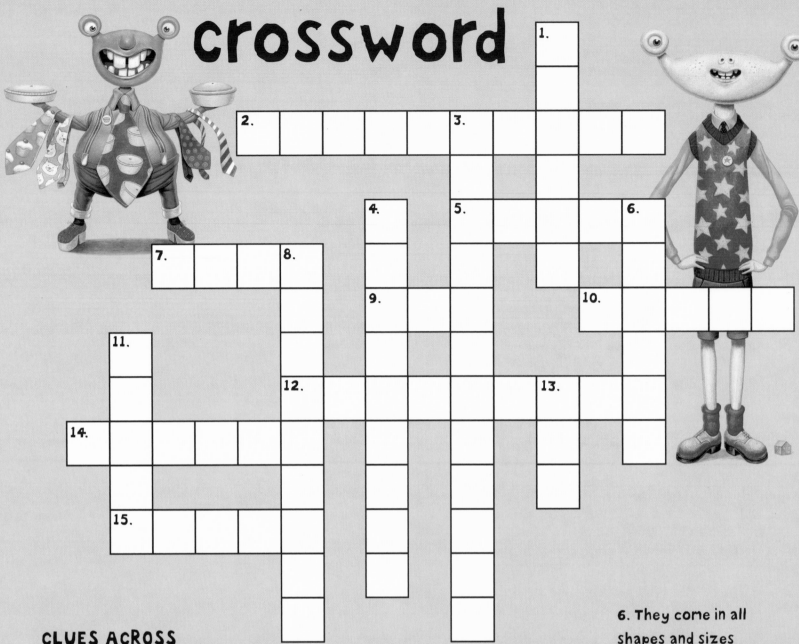

CLUES ACROSS

2. A really tall alien who dreams of long enough trousers (10)

5. Stardust sports _____, a favourite place for the Oooballyballies (5)

7. This planet is red and cold and rocky (4)

9. Bob has to turn his rocket ___ at the end of the day to save the batteries (3)

10. A round and cheesy snack, delicious with pepperoni on top (5)

12. Bob's all-time favourite treat (6,3)

14. An alien named after its two great loves - funky neckwear and savoury baked goods (3,3)

15. Bob's home planet, which the Moon goes round and round (5)

CLUES DOWN

1. A large hole in the Moon's surface, handy for hiding in (6)

3. Very fashionable footwear with a thick, high sole - popular with funky aliens (8,4)

4. An alien which goes everywhere with its identical twin (9)

6. They come in all shapes and sizes apparently, although Bob has never seen one... (6)

8. Bob parks this at the end of every day at Lunar Hill launch-pad (5,4)

11. Another word for alien goo, this is green and disgusting to clean up (5)

13. The one and only Man on the Moon (3)

STUCK? Remember to read Bob's fact pages!

42

We Are Not Amused!

COLOUR IN THIS PORTRAIT OF QUEEN BATTLEAXE III.

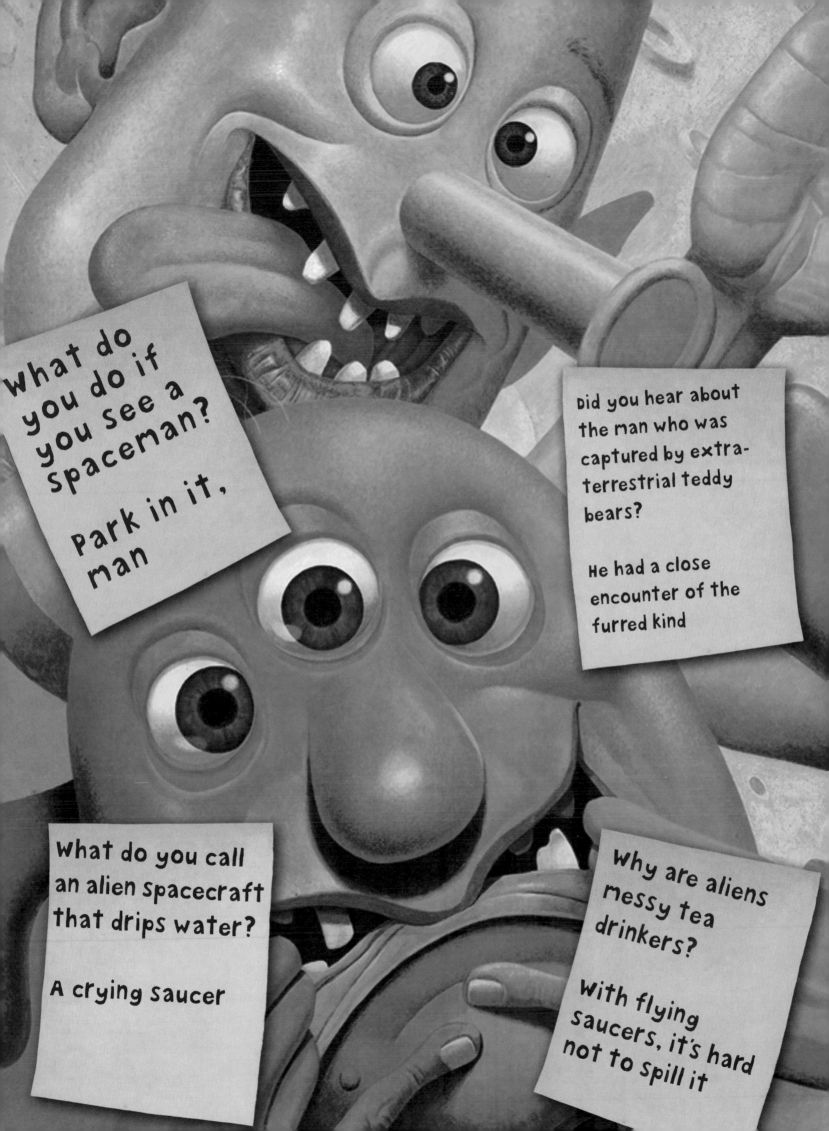

Alien Jokes

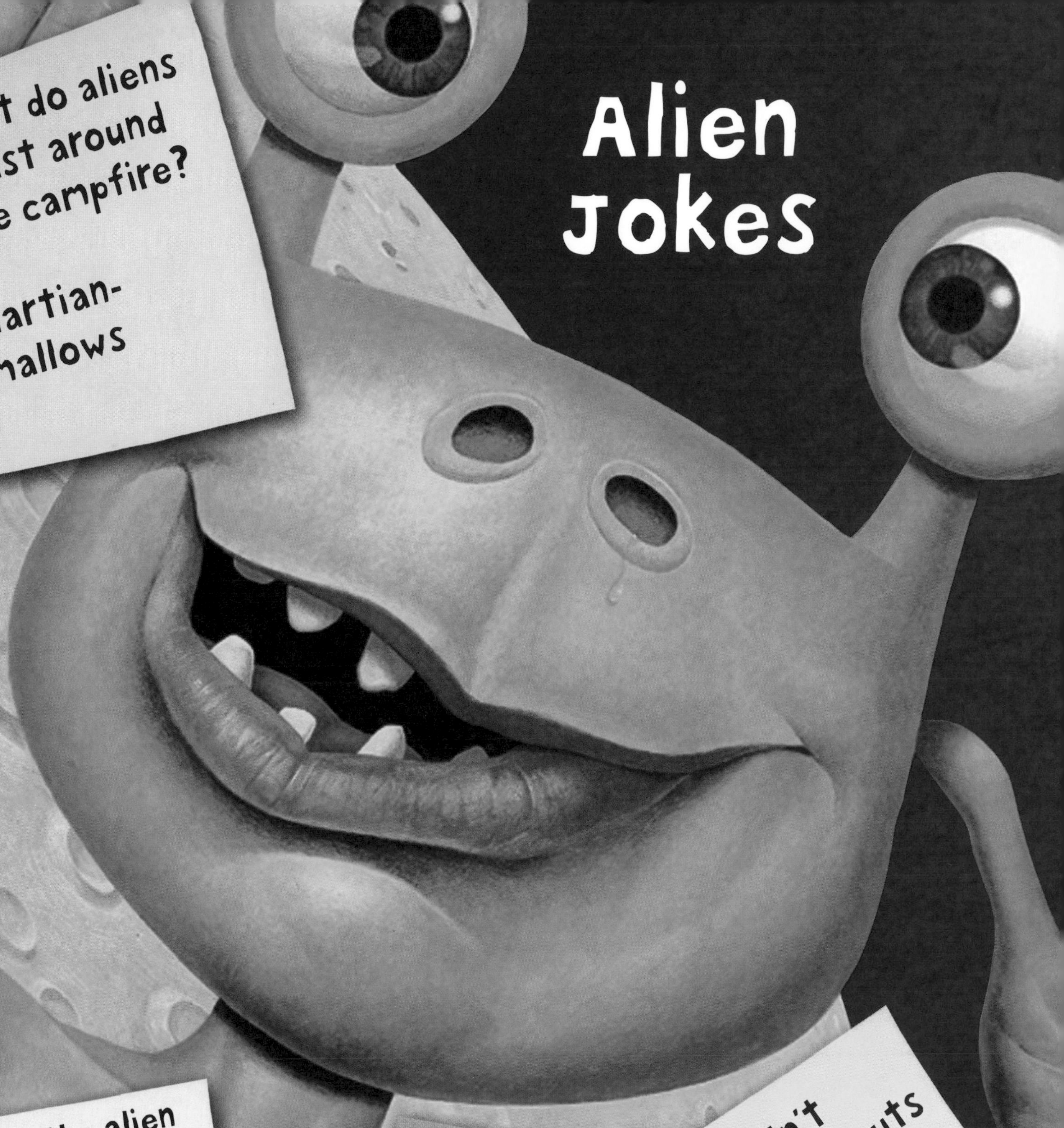

What do aliens toast around the campfire?

Martian-mallows

Why did the alien want to leave the party?

The atmosphere wasn't right

How do you make a baby sleep on a space ship?

You rocket

Why didn't the astronauts stay on the moon?

Because it was full

45

HOW MANY ALIEN TYPES CAN YOU SPOT IN THIS SCENE? CAN YOU SEE BOB TOO?

(ANSWERS ON PAGE 60.)

The Robot Two-Step

COLOUR IN THIS SCENE WHERE MR NIGEL CARRUTHERS TEACHES BOB TO DANCE!

Alien Pets

This is the petshop where I come to buy Barry special treats.
The owner insists all the pets are alien animals - he is obviously trying
to put the prices up. Here are a few of his hilarious 'facts'.

Plutonian Peehop
The Peehop's wild hopping displays should only be watched for a limited time. More than ten minutes could leave you dizzy, queasy or even hypnotised.

Gold-Pronged Glumpuppy
Despite the fact they look, sound and act miserable, Glumpuppies are blissfully happy hounds. They also love scotch eggs.

Pockmarked Jabbapuck
Bred to compete in the annual spacehopper games, Jabbapucks are finely-tuned super-athletes, albeit with peanut-sized brains.

Long-Pronged Girafter
The price of a Girafter varies depending on the length of its neck. Every 10 centimetres costs 26p. The most expensive girafter ever cost **£47.52**.

Hoopnoggin Bear
The Hoopnoggin's head-hoop size changes with its mood. When glum, the hoop almost closes up, but when happy it expands to the size of a hula hoop.

Marzebra
With their red and white stripes, Mars's Marzebras are faster, stronger and more intelligent than their black and white Earth counterparts.

Grizzly Tri-Eye
Whoever named the Grizzy Tri-Eye was not the most observant, failing to spot the fourth eye, disguised as a belly button.

Brilliant Alien Treehanger [BAT]
Treehangers are nothing like Earth's bats. They have **20:20** vision, hate the dark and very rarely turn into vampires.

Butterflop
With the intelligence of the average ten year old boy, Butterflops are beautiful, graceful creatures. It's just a shame they only live for five minutes or so.

CAN YOU SPOT TWENTY ONE DIFFERENCES BETWEEN THE TWO SCENES?

I DOUBT IF BOB CAN!

Lip-Smacking Snacks

If you have been wondering how to create some of Bob's tastiest nibbles, then wonder no more! Here, Bob has kindly provided us with some of his all-time favourite recipes. Before you start, make sure you have a grown-up to help you.

Here Bob is daydreaming about the ultimate super-crumpet!

THE UNIVERSE'S BEST EVER CUP OF TEA AND BUTTERED CRUMPETS

TEA
- Put the kettle on. (Ask a grown up to do this bit.)
- Take a trusty tea bag and put it in a mug (a blue-and-white striped one is best).
- Ask a grown up to pour the boiling water over the bag, then let the tea brew for a minute or so.
- Add a splash of milk and a sugar cube or two.

CRUMPET
- Take two crumpets and ask a grown up to put them in the toaster or under the grill. (Rocket boosters are not suitable for the job as they burn your crumpet to smithereens in seconds.)
- When the crumpet is nicely browned on both sides, ask a grown up to take it out.
- As soon as it's cool enough to touch (your grown up can tell you when) butter thickly.

Recipe courtesy of the Moon-Soup Pit-Stop café

Bob uses his special rocket-shaped teapot for a fuller flavour.

SPECTACULARLY TREMENDOUS GINGERBREAD ASTRONAUTS

INGREDIENTS

350g plain flour • 1 teaspoon ground ginger
1 teaspoon bicarbonate of soda
100g butter or margarine
175g soft light brown sugar
1 egg • 4 tablespoons golden syrup

INSTRUCTIONS

Put the flour, ground ginger, bicarbonate of soda and butter in a mixing bowl. Mix together with your fingertips until everything is nice and crumbly. Add the sugar, syrup and egg and mix until it forms a squidgy ball.

Roll it out with a rolling pin, until it is about 5mm thick. If you dust the ball and the table with flour, the mixture won't stick to it. Cut out some astronaut shapes with a gingerbread man shaped cutter. You could make rocket, planet or pickled onion shapes if you prefer.

Put the shapes onto a baking tray and ask a grown up to put them into the oven at 190 C and take them out after 10-15 minutes.

Once they've cooled on a wire rack, use icing, raisins and chocolate buttons to make their space suits.

Thanks to Vera Crumble for lending Bob these recipes

BOB'S FAVOURITE CHERRY BUN RECIPE

INGREDIENTS

100g butter or margarine • 125g sugar
250g plain flour • 50g glace cherries
3 tablespoons milk • A pinch of salt
1 egg • 2 rounded teaspoons baking powder
100g icing sugar • 2 tablespoons warm water

INSTRUCTIONS

Put the butter and the sugar in a bowl and mix with a fork until you have a creamy paste.

Swizzle the egg and the milk together and pour it into the butter and sugar mix.

Drop the flour through a sifter until it looks like a soft pile of moon dust. Mix in the baking powder, the lovely cherries (saving one to go on the top of each cupcake) and salt.

Now mix all the ingredients and pour the mixture into cake cases. Ask a grown up to put these into the oven at 180 C and take them out after 15-20 minutes.

When the cupcakes have cooled down, make the icing by dribbling the water into the icing sugar and mixing it up until you have a shiny, gluey paste. Pour a spoonful or two over each cupcake and place a lovely red cherry on top. Beautiful!

Flight Night

Use the stickers in the middle of the book to show what's happening while Bob is snoozing.

5... 4... 3... 2... 1... LIFT OFF!

COLOUR IN THIS SCENE OF BOB HEADING OFF TO WORK FROM LUNAR HILL LAUNCH-PAD.

Grand Battle of the Solar System

Roll up, roll up! Welcome to the bad girls and boys of space...

The Pet Catcher

TOOL: Large net

TROUBLE CAUSED: Has often bothered Barry. Bob wonders how he fills his days, looking for alien pets! Ha!

CURRENT THREAT: Significant. Behind his shop counter by day, he prowls the town with his swooping net by night.

Queen Battleaxe III

To my left
In the blue corner
Wearing a blue velvet greatcoat and white ermine stole
Weighing 194 pounds
Fresh from training in the Royal coliseum
Representing the royal dynasty of Good King Giblet
And with previous titles to her name including Princess Giblet
She tops the chart of the best 50 mechanical bull-riders of all time!
An incredible 12 planets have been demolished at her whim!
And with an unbeatable track record for boshing nincompoop spacemen
We are sure to be amused!
Introducing... Her Highness Queen Battleaxe III!

Stan the Man on Gas Mark 5

TOOLS: Ray gun and Incredible Edible Spaceboots

TROUBLE CAUSED: Gave Bob a major headache after inserting Mr Nigel Carruthers' heart of stone.

CURRENT THREAT: None. Humbled and reformed after serving his sentence (a week of unpaid work at Vera Crumble's bakery).

The Stupendous Alacazamo

To my right
In the red corner
Wearing a red top hat and tailcoat with gold braid trim
Weighing 208 pounds
Hailing from 34 Chilblain Lane (just above the ABRA-KEBAB-RA takeaway)
With previous titles including Mr Reginald Stopcock
Currently ranked number one in the Daily Bugle's Magical League
He has changed a free-range chicken into an African elephant!
He has levitated the Reverend Pip's toupee!
He has even temporarily disappeared the Moon!
Ladies and Gentlemen: prepare to be amazed!
Introducing... the Stupendous Alacazamo!

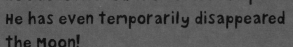

Professor Sickle

TOOL: Clonemaster 4000

TROUBLE CAUSED: Gave Bob a fright by creating clones in his image.

CURRENT THREAT: Minimal. Has since ditched the world of science and become a lonely old woman in a poky flat with a miserable cat.

Join the dots!

FIND OUT WHAT BOB GETS UP TO ON TUESDAY LUNCH BREAKS!

CLUES ACROSS

3. Bob's good friend, the Man on Mars (5)

5. Bob's other good friend, the Man on Saturn (3)

7. A Space Ship (6)

9. A tasty bread-snack, delicious with a cheese, beef-paste or peanut butter filling (8)

11. Bob likes the steak and kidney kind, but it's delicious with apple and custard too (3)

12. A trendy woolly jumper without the arms (4,3)

CLUES DOWN

1. The colour of the sky at night (5)

2. This twinkles in the sky when it gets dark (4)

3. You need a good pair of these for walking on the Moon (5)

4. Don't forget to pick one of these up from Vera Crumble's bakery on your way to Tarantula Van Trumpet's office (4)

6. The outfit Bob wears to work (4,4)

8. An outdoor feast with cherry buns, fish-paste sandwiches and pickled onions (6)

10. If you get close to the Sun you'll probably feel like this (3)

12. A lovely cup of this is best taken with a biscuit (or two) (3)

(ANSWERS ON PAGE 60.)

crossword

Problem solved!

Here are the answers to all of Bob's puzzling puzzles.

Maze

Alien Spotter

Spot The Difference

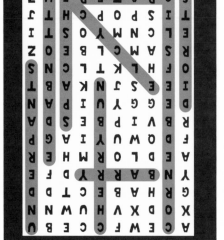

Oh, My Word

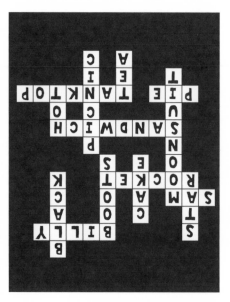

Crossword 2

Crossword 1